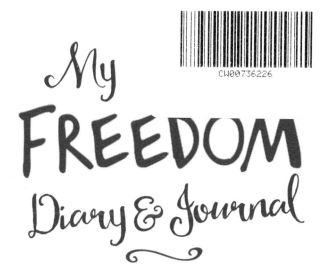

My FREEDOM Diary & Journal

Julia Keys AND Jacqui Coles

Authors of the number 1 bestselling relationship book
The MAN*Script*

Hashtag PRESS

This edition published in Great Britain by Hashtag Press 2018

Text copyright © Julia Keys and Jacqueline Coles 2018
Copyright Cover illustration © Helen Braid 2018
Copyright Cover concept © Kate Turner 2018

The moral right of the author has been asserted

All rights reserved. No part of this publication may be reproduced, stored in retrieval system, or transmitted, in any form or by any means without the prior written permission of the publisher, nor be otherwise circulated in any form of binding or cover other than that in which it is published and without a similar condition being imposed on the subsequent purchaser.

A CIP catalogue for this book is available from the British Library.

ISBN 978-0-9957806-1-3

Typeset in Garamond Classic 11.25/14 by Blaze Typesetting

Printed in Great Britain by Clays Ltd, Elcograf S.p.A

Hashtag PRESS

HASHTAG PRESS BOOKS
Hashtag Press Ltd
Kent, England, United Kingdom
Email: info@hashtagpress.co.uk
Website: www.hashtagpress.co.uk
Twitter: @hashtag_press

Help free yourself from the emotional pain of a relationship crisis, step by step, day by day, in your own time and at your own pace. . .

My Freedom Diary & Journal
Belongs to:

If found, please return to:

"Think about any attachments that are
depleting your emotional reserves.
Consider letting them go."
- Oprah Winfrey -

Introduction

My Freedom Diary & Journal is your own private place to offload what you think and feel, without worrying about what people may think or feel about you. It is not easy to heal from the heartbreak of betrayal and move to a place where you can be happy and back in control of your life.

To have the best chance of achieving happiness and regaining control of your life, you need to begin to accept what has happened and what that now means. It's really hard to accept the negative impact that the actions of others have on you, particularly if the impact affects your lifestyle, the way you live—or used to live.

Equally, the loss of a loved one can create such a void in your life, that you feel like it will never be filled. It can be overwhelming, lonely and unbearable. It can also be difficult to reconnect with your own identity, after you have been one-half of a relationship.

My Freedom Diary & Journal will help you write your own recovery story and re-adjust to the life you are now facing. Your own words will help you see how you can heal and what you need to do, so that you can survive and thrive, with or without your partner. Only when you put yourself in the driving seat, will you have the power to take control of your life and make it what you want it to be.

My Freedom Diary & Journal is designed to help you free yourself from the emotional pain of betrayal and get back in touch with what you need in order to feel complete. It is a day-by-day, step-by-step guide to get you through the hurtful times and move you forward into a space where once again you can be happy and empowered.

We not only want you to survive being cheated on, but to thrive as a result, for this is your chance to discover what is right for your life.

One of the best ways to deal with hurt and negative emotions is to write them down. As you progress on your road to recovery, you will be able to look back at your own words and see just how far you have come. It is initially hard to accept, but being able to reflect on your own story will help you to realise you are stronger than you ever thought possible.

Be your own best friend. The more you write positive things about yourself and reflect on those words, the more they will become part of you and the more likely they are to become true.

One of the hardest things to come to terms with, following a betrayal, is the misconceived thought that you didn't matter enough to the other person. This feeling can stall your recovery. Throughout this diary, we remind you regularly that you do matter, because you do!

Every day, remind yourself that the past is the past. It's time to re-focus on the present. You matter and you must keep looking forward. *You can do it, you can be happy.*

"The best is yet to be. . ."
Robert Browning
1812 - 1889

How to use

My Freedom Diary & Journal

Each section in My Freedom Diary & Journal is designed to help you work through your thoughts and feelings. You will get the most out of your diary if you are honest with yourself. There is no need for pretence here, just say it as it is.

Don't hold back, write it all down, no matter how angry or hurt you feel towards the person(s) involved, or even at yourself. The words need to be released from your thoughts and your emotions and given a safe outlet. This is your private diary, for you and you alone to see.

You can work at your own pace, there is no timeframe to work through My Freedom Diary & Journal.

There is a section at the beginning where we guide you to write a letter(s) to the person or people enabling you to tell them exactly how you feel. This is your opportunity to express all your hurt, anger, frustration, regret, sadness, loss, love and any other emotion. Make sure you clearly name the person or people, as if you were talking to them. Once written, fold it and place it in one of the pages at the front of the book. It now belongs in the past and your future is within your power to achieve—it's what you make it. Keep looking forward.

Just remember, life goes on regardless of whether you choose to move on into the unknown or stay trapped in the past, wondering what could have been. Your energy is precious, don't waste it on those who don't deserve it and don't let life pass you by. It's easy to get trapped by the past, but this is your chance to set yourself free; you owe it to yourself.

Towards the middle of My Freedom Diary & Journal, you will see the following:

Today I am—Acknowledge how you feel

Today I will—State the action you need to take

Today I have—Note what you have achieved

Gratitude note—Write a note to someone or something you are grateful for that day

You can do this exercise as often as you like although we recommend you try it for a few weeks on a daily basis to start with. There are questions to help you reflect how the previous seven days have been for you. That week is now over and in the past. Keep looking forward. Again, there is no rulebook for how you choose to use My Freedom Diary & Journal, it's entirely up to you to take control of your own recovery schedule. We are here to help and guide. You can start each new day with the 'Just for Now' thought and apply it to your life.

At the back of My Freedom Diary & Journal, you have space to fill out diary entries for the year. You can write as much as you want. It's a safe space to explore how you feel.

If you have recently been betrayed and had your heart broken, you will most likely relate to most, if not all of the statements below. However, we would also like to say that this exercise will help anyone who is going through the feelings of being let down, and deceived by someone else.

Look at each statement and give it a score between one and five. For example, write one if the statement fully describes how you feel; write five if it is the complete opposite of how you feel. If you are somewhere between one and five, write the number which most appropriately describes where you are currently.

The statements are:

1. My head is so full of thoughts, I can't think straight.
2. I can't stop thinking about him/her/them.
3. I can't focus on anything.
4. I can't eat, sleep or function properly.
5. I don't want to socialise or see anyone.
6. I can't face life with or without him/her.
7. I can't trust anyone.
8. I can't trust myself.
9. I can never get over this pain.
10. It hurts so much.
11. I can't accept what has happened.
12. I will never be happy again.
13. I am to blame.
14. I hate him/her.
15. I feel so alone.

Once you have given a score to each question, add up your total. Once you've done that, put your score away somewhere safe. Do not think about your scores again until you reach the end of the journal. Then, come back to these questions and ask yourself the same questions. Re-score your answers and compare it to your original answers. We know you will be surprised by how far you have travelled.

> *"There will come a time when you believe*
> *everything is finished. That will*
> *be the beginning."*
> **Louis L'Amour**
> **1908 - 1988**

The Release Letter

Grab a piece of paper and write down what you would like to say to the people that have hurt you. There are some examples of sentence openers below. The idea is not to send it to them but instead to safely release your thoughts and feelings.

My release letter to. . .

I am writing this because. . .

You have hurt me by. . .

I wish you had done. . .

Moving forward I want. . .

The negatives about the person and the relationship

The positives about the person and the relationship

*"Worrying doesn't empty tomorrow of
its sorrow, it empties today of
its strength."*
Corrie ten Boom
1892 - 1983

Why you Shouldn't Worry Anymore

Worrying serves no purpose other than to create anxiety, so you need to direct your worry into action. Taking action reduces the worry and therefore, the strain upon your physical and mental wellbeing.

Without action, your worries have nowhere to go and make you more and more anxious. To find a solution to your worries, it may help to talk to a trusted friend or ask for help from an appropriate professional such as a doctor, lawyer or counsellor.

What has happened has happened, you cannot change the past. It's now your future that you have to focus on.

Your worries may include finances, children, work, health, and/or family. To think about them all collectively can be overwhelming, particularly in the middle of the night when everything snowballs and grows to unrealistic proportions. Rather than focus on the worrying, you need to try and focus on solutions—bit by bit.

There are three things that you need to acknowledge in order to get your worries into perspective.

The three things are:

1. The situations you have **NO** control over (you need to look hard at finding even a tiny solution when you feel you have no control—that solution may well simply be acceptance).
2. The situations you have **SOME** control over (take strength from the control that you do have).
3. The situations you have **FULL** control over (full control is when the decision is one hundred percent your own, so be sure that you're making the right choice and ask yourself, "Does it feel right?").

If you are having trouble accepting the situations which you cannot control, list them and ask for help. A worry out is better than a worry in.

On the next page start listing the situations you have no, some and full control over.

I Matter

The situations I have **NO** control over

The situations I have **SOME** control over (try to list them in priority order and think about them one at a time, otherwise you will be overwhelmed).

The situations I have **FULL** control over

*"I know for sure that what we
dwell on is what we become."*
Oprah Winfrey

Changing Negative Thoughts

Focusing on regret, wishful thinking and self-blame keeps you stuck in the past. If your partner did not tell you how he/she was feeling, how could you know what to do about it?

Constantly thinking about negative situations can lead to a person becoming depressed. It is not always easy, but it is so important to focus on the positives and to challenge all your negative thoughts.

You must not blame yourself for negative experiences, but by learning from them, you can be kind to yourself, which means you can then stop all blame, all guilt, all punishment and all pain.

Here, we show you how to change the most common, false self-beliefs into empowering positive thoughts that will move you forward.

Remember—YOU MATTER!

False belief	True belief
It was my fault he had an affair	It was his choice to have an affair
I can't trust anyone	I can trust myself

False belief	True belief
I should have been able to prevent it	The responsibility for his/her choices was not mine
I should have been able to handle the situation	How can I be expected to handle a situation I knew nothing about?
I should be over this by now	It takes time to heal, usually far longer than I think
I can't stand these feelings	These feelings are telling me I need to let go
I feel everything is out of my control	It is within my power to take control
No-one cares	It is my responsibility to take care of myself
The future looks bleak	The future will be as good as the effort I put into it
I feel locked in the past	I will take positive action to keep moving forward
I am not good enough	I am good enough in every way
No-one will want me	It is my choice to have a relationship or not
I don't matter	I MATTER
I am powerless	I have the POWER

*"As soon as you trust yourself, you will
know how to live."*
Johann Wolfgang von Goethe
1749 - 1832

Learning to Trust Again

Trust can be regained and rebuilt. The most important trust to focus on is the trust you have within yourself. This is why we have not only asked who you don't trust, but we've asked you to list the people who you trust and those who trust you. This will help you realise that you matter to other people.

Recognising these people and what you mean to them will help you to start trusting yourself again and appreciate how valuable you are.

Complete the following:

People I don't trust—why don't I trust them?

People I trust—why do I trust them?

People who trust me—why do they trust me?

Now complete the following:

Examples of times when my gut feeling/instinct has been right

Things I will accept, going forward

Things I will not accept, going forward

*"I'm not afraid of storms, for I am
learning how to sail my ship."*
Mary Louise Alcott
1832 - 1888

Letting Go

Letting go of painful feelings doesn't come easily. It takes time and a willingness to accept what's happened. It also requires a desire to be rid of the negative feelings that can plague your life on a daily basis.

Reliving your worst moments, over and over again, is like picking at a wound and never allowing it to heal. Once you start to let go, that wound will slowly close. Accept that if you don't let go, you can't go forward. You will remain stuck.

Here are some questions to ask yourself to start the process of letting go:

Which person(s) do I need to let go of to create a space for new people to come into my life?

What feelings/emotions/fears/beliefs/memories/situations do I need to let go of to give me peace of mind?

What do I need to let go of to help me feel strong?

What negative feelings do I need to release?

What am I frightened of?

Who can I turn to for help?

*"I realise there's something incredibly honest
about trees in winter, how they're
experts at letting things go."*
Jeffrey McDaniel

I Matter

*"Always forgive your enemies; nothing
annoys them so much."*
Oscar Wilde
1854 - 1900

Learning to Accept and Forgive

The moment you can start to accept your situation and the hand you have been dealt, is the moment you will be able to release the feelings of resentment, which trap you in the past. You can then start the healing process. Without acceptance, you will be in a constant state of conflict, which can rob you of so much energy, leaving you emotionally drained and tired.

Whether you stay with your partner or not, the sooner you accept what has happened and focus on yourself, the earlier you will be on the road to recovery and freedom.

For the majority of people, forgiveness is one of the hardest things to achieve; particularly if you have been left in a vulnerable situation. Forgiveness is about releasing your negative feelings, not condoning the behaviour of the person(s) who hurt you.

Whatever happened, has happened. Holding on keeps the pain alive—letting go releases it.

You owe it to yourself to let the pain go and create a space for happiness to come into your life. The longer you hold on, the deeper the resentment may become.

Ask yourself:

Is what I am feeling about that person(s) good for me?

What do I need to accept?

What can I do to help me accept where I am now?

What do I need to change to help me accept?

·

You may never be able to fully forgive, but if you can forgive the person(s) even a little bit, it will go some way to helping you heal.

Who is the person(s) I need to try and forgive?

How would it feel not to carry around resentment and bitterness?

Can I accept that the burden of betrayal is not mine to carry, but the person who cheated on me?

I Matter

"Love yourself first and everything else falls into line. You really have to love yourself to get anything done in this world."

Lucille Ball

1911 - 1989

Self-Care: Being Kind to Yourself

The most important thing you can do right now is to take care of you. Ask yourself how you would treat a friend or family member who was going through the same thing? You would be kind, caring and regularly reminding them to look after themselves. That is exactly what you have to do now, but for yourself. You will manage your hurt more easily if you show yourself compassion and celebrate what is good in your life.

There is a child in all of us who needs to be loved and cared for, none more so than when they've been hurt and betrayed. Love and soothe your inner child and you will naturally be learning to love yourself.

You must be gentle, kind and patient with yourself.

Simple tips to help you take care of YOU:

- Practice self-compassion. Stop criticising yourself. Apply kindness, not self-criticism.
- Stay connected with the outside world.
- Find something to be grateful for each day.
- Seek out people/activities that make you smile.

- Surround yourself with positive people.
- Learn to praise yourself and congratulate yourself for getting through the day.
- Visualise yourself feeling strong and in control of your life.
- Reconnect with yourself. What are your strengths and talents?
- Eat little and often and as healthily as you can.
- Drink plenty of water, particularly when drinking alcohol (keep alcohol to a minimum).
- Take regular exercise—get out for a walk every day, even if you can't face doing anything else.
- Accept we all make mistakes. By learning from them, you allow yourself to know what is right for you.
- Try to stay focused on looking forward.
- Simplify your commitments, so you don't over burden yourself.
- Take plenty of rest.

Now, please answer the following:

What are my strengths?

What are my talents?

Who/what makes me smile?

What activity can I do to make me feel better?

What areas need to change for my life to improve?

"It's not the mountain we conquer,
but ourselves."
Sir Edmund Hillary
1919 - 2008

Healing Beliefs

- I have an open heart to new opportunities
- I have power
- I am willing to love and be loved
- I have a new chapter in my life
- I forgive myself
- I am calm and in control
- I am safe
- I am positive about my future and can let go of fear
- I do not use the word 'humiliated' anymore
- I have clarity and focus
- I am not to blame
- I am better than wanting revenge
- I am open to trusting again
- I have no reason to feel jealous
- I will forgive, to set myself free
- I am brave, courageous and have nothing to fear
- I am confident in my appearance and who I am
- I see myself happy
- I am at peace
- I approve of myself
- I am loveable

*"Your time is limited, so don't waste it
living someone else's life. . ."*
Steve Jobs
1955 - 2011

Time for You

In order to maximise your day, in line with the goals you want to achieve for yourself, you need to think about how much of your time is spent on others. The ability to multi-task can be very useful, but it can lead to a lack of focus on more important things that require your attention.

If there were no other considerations in your life, how you would like to spend your day?

How much of your day do you give to you?

How much of your day do you give to others?

What can you change to create more time for you?

*"A goal is a dream
with a deadline."*
Napoleon Hill
1883 - 1970

Goals to Help you Move Forward

Depending on where you are in your recovery, your daily goal maybe something as simple as getting out of bed to attending a networking event or party. Implementing a few changes can help get you where you want to be. Take small steps towards each goal. Any long-term goals need to be broken down into achievable, bite-size pieces. For example, if you need to buy food, just buy food for that day. Don't worry too much about what will be on the menu tomorrow. . . or next week!

Remember, no matter how small, it's important to celebrate all your achievements and reflect on how they made you feel. Share your success with people you trust. This will help to motivate you to keep going forward to achieve your bigger goals.

Ask yourself:

What are my long-term goals?

I Matter

What short-term goals can I put in place to achieve my long-term goals?

What will be different in my life if I achieve my goals?

What is a realistic time frame for my goals to be achieved?

Are my goals about what is right for me and not about changing someone else?

Are my goals realistic?

Are my goals under my control?

If this was a friend's goals, what would I advise him/her to do to get started?

How will I know I am making progress?

*"Gratitude is the healthiest of all human emotions.
The more you express gratitude for what you
have, the more likely you will have even
more to express gratitude for."*
Zig Ziglar
1926 - 2012

Things to be Grateful For

Saying "thank you" isn't just a nice thing to do for someone else, it's a great thing to do for you. Betrayal takes from you, but gratitude gives back to you. Being thankful helps you to recognise the important things and people that surround you. Gratitude lifts you up when you are feeling down. Notice and appreciate the simple and ordinary things in your life. Appreciate the moment, because the moment you are in is one step closer to your long-term goals and happiness.

On the next page, make a list of the people and things you are grateful for. It could be the roof over your head, your favourite song playing on the radio, your child making you a cup of tea, the sun shining in your garden. Try to end your day with a thankful note. Before you go to sleep at night, go through your gratitude list to express what you have been thankful for that day.

My Gratitude List

I Matter

"You are today where your thoughts have brought you; you will be tomorrow where your thoughts take you."
James Allen
1864 - 1912

Week 1

Just for now I am brave

Today I am

Today I will

Today I have

My daily gratitude note:

I Matter

Just for now it is in my power to change my thoughts

Today I am

Today I will

Today I have

My daily gratitude note:

Just for now I embrace the things I have achieved

Today I am

Today I will

Today I have

My daily gratitude note:

I Matter

Just for now I am in control

Today I am

Today I will

Today I have

 My daily gratitude note:

Just for now I care about me

Today I am

Today I will

Today I have

 My daily gratitude note:

I Matter

Just for now I am hopeful

Today I am

Today I will

Today I have

🦋 My daily gratitude note:

Just for now I value who I am

Today I am

Today I will

Today I have

 My daily gratitude note:

Julia Keys and Jacqui Coles

Reflections page
Remember YOU matter

What have I achieved this week?

Who/what am I most grateful for?

What have I done to work towards reaching my goals?

What do I need to do to get me through the next week?

Keep Looking Forward   42

Week 2

Just for now I have the ability to make the right choices

Today I am

Today I will

Today I have

 My daily gratitude note:

I Matter

Just for now I choose to let go of the past

Today I am

Today I will

Today I have

 My daily gratitude note:

Just for now I focus on today

Today I am

Today I will

Today I have

 My daily gratitude note:

I Matter

Just for now I acknowledge my deepest fears

Today I am

Today I will

Today I have

> 🦋 My daily gratitude note:

Just for now I remember when I received praise

Today I am

Today I will

Today I have

My daily gratitude note:

I Matter

Just for now I am important

Today I am

Today I will

Today I have

 My daily gratitude note:

Just for now I will enjoy the time I have on my own

Today I am

Today I will

Today I have

My daily gratitude note:

Reflections page
Remember YOU matter

What have I achieved this week?

Who/what am I most grateful for?

What have I done to work towards reaching my goals?

What do I need to do to get me through the next week?

Week 3

Just for now I accept what I don't know

Today I am

Today I will

Today I have

My daily gratitude note:

I Matter

Just for now I am thankful for my friends

Today I am

Today I will

Today I have

 My daily gratitude note:

Just for now I accept I am vulnerable

Today I am

Today I will

Today I have

My daily gratitude note:

Just for now I am proud of who I am

Today I am

Today I will

Today I have

 My daily gratitude note:

Just for now I value those who care about me

Today I am

Today I will

Today I have

My daily gratitude note:

I Matter

Just for now I have the courage to pursue my dreams

Today I am

Today I will

Today I have

🦋 My daily gratitude note:

Just for now I will let go of the people who drag me down

Today I am

Today I will

Today I have

My daily gratitude note:

I Matter

Reflections page
Remember YOU matter

What have I achieved this week?

Who/what am I most grateful for?

What have I done to work towards reaching my goals?

What do I need to do to get me through the next week?

Week 4

Just for now I will let go of resentment and set myself free

Today I am

Today I will

Today I have

 My daily gratitude note:

I Matter

Just for now I will create the future I desire

Today I am

Today I will

Today I have

 My daily gratitude note:

Just for now I value the lessons I am learning

Today I am

Today I will

Today I have

My daily gratitude note:

I Matter

Just for now I value honesty and integrity

Today I am

Today I will

Today I have

> 🦋 My daily gratitude note:

Just for now I value myself

Today I am

Today I will

Today I have

 My daily gratitude note:

I Matter

Just for now I accept the ups and downs of my life

Today I am

Today I will

Today I have

My daily gratitude note:

Just for now I am proud of myself

Today I am

Today I will

Today I have

My daily gratitude note:

I Matter

Reflections page
Remember YOU matter

What have I achieved this week?

Who/what am I most grateful for?

What have I done to work towards reaching my goals?

What do I need to do to get me through the next week?

Week 5
Just for now I forgive myself

Today I am

Today I will

Today I have

🦋 My daily gratitude note:

I Matter

Just for now I deserve to be respected

Today I am

Today I will

Today I have

 My daily gratitude note:

Just for now I will have time for me

Today I am

Today I will

Today I have

My daily gratitude note:

I Matter

Just for now I will face the truth

Today I am

Today I will

Today I have

 My daily gratitude note:

Just for now I accept the changes in my life

Today I am

Today I will

Today I have

My daily gratitude note:

I Matter

Just for now I will be kind to myself

Today I am

Today I will

Today I have

 My daily gratitude note:

Just for now I will put myself first

Today I am

Today I will

Today I have

My daily gratitude note:

I Matter

Reflections page
Remember YOU matter

What have I achieved this week?

Who/what am I most grateful for?

What have I done to work towards reaching my goals?

What do I need to do to get me through the next week?

Week 6
Just for now I will treat myself

Today I am

Today I will

Today I have

 My daily gratitude note:

Just for now I value the good times

Today I am

Today I will

Today I have

My daily gratitude note:

Just for now I will create the future I desire

Today I am

Today I will

Today I have

My daily gratitude note:

I Matter

Just for now I will never give up

Today I am

Today I will

Today I have

 My daily gratitude note:

Just for now I will keep looking forward

Today I am

Today I will

Today I have

My daily gratitude note:

I Matter

Just for now I value myself

Today I am

Today I will

Today I have

My daily gratitude note:

Just for now I am my thoughts

Today I am

Today I will

Today I have

🦋 My daily gratitude note:

Reflections page
Remember YOU matter

What have I achieved this week?

Who/what am I most grateful for?

What have I done to work towards reaching my goals?

What do I need to do to get me through the next week?

Week 7

Just for now I embrace the small things

Today I am

Today I will

Today I have

My daily gratitude note:

I Matter

Just for now I am thankful for what I have

Today I am

Today I will

Today I have

 My daily gratitude note:

Just for now I can be happy

Today I am

Today I will

Today I have

My daily gratitude note:

I Matter

Just for now I can do it

Today I am

Today I will

Today I have

My daily gratitude note:

Just for now I enjoy the little things

Today I am

Today I will

Today I have

🦋 My daily gratitude note:

Just for now I embrace the moment

Today I am

Today I will

Today I have

 My daily gratitude note:

Just for now I show myself compassion

Today I am

Today I will

Today I have

My daily gratitude note:

I Matter

Reflections page
Remember YOU matter

What have I achieved this week?

Who/what am I most grateful for?

What have I done to work towards reaching my goals?

What do I need to do to get me through the next week?

Week 8

Just for now I will focus on my goal for the week

Today I am

Today I will

Today I have

 My daily gratitude note:

Just for now I am confident

Today I am

Today I will

Today I have

 My daily gratitude note:

Just for now I will protect myself

Today I am

Today I will

Today I have

🦋 My daily gratitude note:

I Matter

Just for now I will celebrate the life I have

Today I am

Today I will

Today I have

🦋 My daily gratitude note:

Just for now I value truth

Today I am

Today I will

Today I have

 My daily gratitude note:

Just for now I accept the obstacles

Today I am

Today I will

Today I have

🦋 My daily gratitude note:

Just for now I will let go of painful attachments

Today I am

Today I will

Today I have

My daily gratitude note:

Reflections page
Remember YOU matter

What have I achieved this week?

Who/what am I most grateful for?

What have I done to work towards reaching my goals?

What do I need to do to get me through the next week?

Week 9
Just for now I will count my blessings

Today I am

Today I will

Today I have

 My daily gratitude note:

Just for now I do my best

Today I am

Today I will

Today I have

 My daily gratitude note:

Just for now I acknowledge my progress

Today I am

Today I will

Today I have

> My daily gratitude note:

I Matter

Just for now I trust my own judgement

Today I am

Today I will

Today I have

My daily gratitude note:

Just for now I have the courage to face my fears

Today I am

Today I will

Today I have

My daily gratitude note:

I Matter

Just for now I am safe to express my feelings

Today I am

Today I will

Today I have

 My daily gratitude note:

Just for now I know I am successful

Today I am

Today I will

Today I have

My daily gratitude note:

I Matter

Reflections page
Remember YOU matter

What have I achieved this week?

Who/what am I most grateful for?

What have I done to work towards reaching my goals?

What do I need to do to get me through the next week?

Week 10

Just for now I am grateful for all that I have

Today I am

Today I will

Today I have

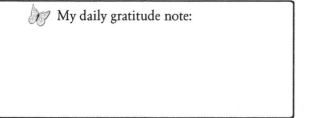

My daily gratitude note:

Just for now I will attract the people I need

Today I am

Today I will

Today I have

 My daily gratitude note:

Just for now I will not be angry

Today I am

Today I will

Today I have

 My daily gratitude note:

I Matter

Just for now I will not judge myself

Today I am

Today I will

Today I have

My daily gratitude note:

Just for now I give myself permission to be free

Today I am

Today I will

Today I have

My daily gratitude note:

Just for now I am willing to move forward

Today I am

Today I will

Today I have

My daily gratitude note:

Just for now I will release the guilt

Today I am

Today I will

Today I have

> 🦋 My daily gratitude note:

Reflections page
Remember YOU matter

What have I achieved this week?

Who/what am I most grateful for?

What have I done to work towards reaching my goals?

What do I need to do to get me through the next week?

Week 11

Just for now I will release the desire for revenge

Today I am

Today I will

Today I have

 My daily gratitude note:

I Matter

Just for now I will laugh

Today I am

Today I will

Today I have

 My daily gratitude note:

Just for now I will let go of the feelings that trap me

Today I am

Today I will

Today I have

```
┌─────────────────────────────────────────────────────────┐
│        🦋  My daily gratitude note:                      │
│                                                           │
│                                                           │
│                                                           │
│                                                           │
└─────────────────────────────────────────────────────────┘
```

I Matter

Just for now I will create new and positive thoughts about my future

Today I am

Today I will

Today I have

🦋 My daily gratitude note:

Just for now I am willing to take the next step

Today I am

Today I will

Today I have

🦋 My daily gratitude note:

I Matter

Just for now I will see the best in everyone

Today I am

Today I will

Today I have

 My daily gratitude note:

Just for now I am receptive to all that is good

Today I am

Today I will

Today I have

> My daily gratitude note:

I Matter

Reflections page
Remember YOU matter

What have I achieved this week?

Who/what am I most grateful for?

What have I done to work towards reaching my goals?

What do I need to do to get me through the next week?

Week 12

Just for now I will express myself freely

Today I am

Today I will

Today I have

 My daily gratitude note:

I Matter

Just for now I will ask for support

Today I am

Today I will

Today I have

 My daily gratitude note:

Just for now I will be patient with myself

Today I am

Today I will

Today I have

My daily gratitude note:

I Matter

Just for now I will be patient with others

Today I am

Today I will

Today I have

 My daily gratitude note:

Just for now I will not doubt myself

Today I am

Today I will

Today I have

My daily gratitude note:

Just for now I will release the desire to criticise others

Today I am

Today I will

Today I have

┌───┐
│   🦋 My daily gratitude note: │
│   │
│   │
│   │
└───┘

Just for now I see only beauty around me

Today I am

Today I will

Today I have

> My daily gratitude note:

Reflections page
Remember YOU matter

What have I achieved this week?

Who/what am I most grateful for?

What have I done to work towards reaching my goals?

What do I need to do to get me through the next week?

"Never, never, never give up."
Winston Churchill
1874 - 1965

I Matter

"Forget what hurt you in the past, but
never forget what it taught you."
Shannon Ladler, Author

Let's Reflect on the Last Three Months

What have I achieved?

Who/what am I most grateful for?

How am I doing towards reaching my goals?

What do I need to do to get me through the coming weeks?

"Happiness is a choice. Peace is a
state of mind. Both are free!"
Amy Leigh Mercree

REMEMBER

Let go of your sadness and embrace new beginnings,
one step at a time.

YOU MATTER

The past cannot be changed, but the future is in
MY POWER

Now re-visit the questions you asked yourself at the beginning of My Freedom Diary & Journal as shown below and re-score your answers.

The questions are:

1. My head is so full of thoughts, I can't think straight
2. I can't stop thinking about him/her/them
3. I can't focus on anything
4. I can't eat, sleep or function properly
5. I don't want to socialise or see anyone
6. I can't face life with or without him/her
7. I can't trust anyone
8. I can't trust myself
9. I can never get over this pain
10. It hurts so much
11. I can't accept what has happened
12. I will never be happy again
13. I am to blame
14. I hate him/her
15. I feel so alone

"Be happy in the moment, that's enough. Each moment is all we need, not more."
Mother Teresa

My One-Year
Freedom Diary

January

SURVIVE

$\mathcal{S}$ o. . . it's about you now

$\mathcal{U}$ nderstand your feelings

$\mathcal{R}$ espect yourself

$\mathcal{V}$ alue who you are

$\mathcal{I}$ dentify your strengths

$\mathcal{V}$ isualise your hopes and dreams

$\mathcal{E}$ mbrace every opportunity

January 1st

January 2nd

I Matter

January 3rd

January 4th

January 5th

January 6th

I Matter

January 7th

January 8th

January 9th

January 10th

I Matter

January 11th

January 12th

January 13th

January 14th

I Matter

January 15th

January 16th

January 17th

January 18th

I Matter

January 19th

January 20th

January 21st

January 22nd

I Matter

January 23rd

January 24th

January 25th

January 26th

I Matter

January 27th

January 28th

January 29th

January 30th

I Matter

January 31st

February

THRIVE!

$\mathcal{T}$ ake time for yourself

$\mathcal{H}$ ave hope for the future

$\mathcal{R}$ emember your achievements

$\mathcal{I}$ dentify how far you have come

$\mathcal{V}$ ery important person—you!

$\mathcal{E}$ very moment is an opportunity to feel empowered

I Matter

February 1st

February 2nd

February 3rd

February 4th

I Matter

February 5th

February 6th

February 7th

February 8th

I Matter

February 9th

February 10th

February 11th

February 12th

I Matter

February 13th

February 14th
Valentine's Day

Valentine's Day

Seeing red hearts everywhere you go when dealing with a break up is really tough.

Valentine's Day can trigger extreme feelings of grief and loss. Use the loss to focus on what the relationship taught you and use it in a positive way.

On Valentine's Day please remember to:

- Stay focused on your future—try to avoid filling your mind with memories of the past.

- Keep things in perspective—it's only one day! And a totally commercially driven day at that!

- Be kind to yourself—book a massage or treat yourself in some other way.

- Keep yourself distracted by work, friends or tasks.

- Stay away from social media.

- Talk to your friends/family about how you feel—don't bottle it up!

February 15th

February 16th

February 17th

February 18th

I Matter

February 19th

February 20th

February 21st

February 22nd

I Matter

February 23rd

February 24th

February 25th

February 26th

I Matter

February 27th

February 28th *(and February 29th if it's a leap year!)*

March

ACTION!

Always stay in the moment

Create your own opportunities

Take time for you

It's never too late

Open your heart

Nurture your inner strength

I Matter

March 1st

March 2nd

March 3rd

March 4th

I Matter

March 5th

March 6th

March 7th

March 8th

I Matter

March 9th

March 10th

March 11th

March 12th

I Matter

March 13th

March 14th

March 15th

March 16th

I Matter

March 17th

March 18th

March 19th

March 20th

I Matter

March 21st

March 22nd

March 23rd

March 24th

I Matter

March 25th

March 26th

March 27th

March 28th

I Matter

March 29th

March 30th

March 31st

I Matter

April

I MATTER!

$\mathcal{I}$ really do

$\mathcal{M}$ y new life

$\mathcal{A}$ ppreciate all that you have

$\mathcal{T}$ rust your instincts

$\mathcal{T}$ ake pride in who you are

$\mathcal{E}$ very thought you have is creating your future

$\mathcal{R}$ elax—you've got this

April 1st

April 2nd

I Matter

April 3rd

April 4th

April 5th

April 6th

I Matter

April 7th

April 8th

April 9th

April 10th

I Matter

April 11th

April 12th

April 13th

April 14th

I Matter

April 15th

April 16th

April 17th

April 18th

I Matter

April 19th

April 20th

April 21st

April 22nd

I Matter

April 23rd

April 24th

April 25th

April 26th

I Matter

April 27th

April 28th

April 29th

April 30th

I Matter

May

GOALS!

G ive yourself a hug

O ther people's opinions don't matter

A im high—you can do it

L ittle steps lead to success

S hine bright

May 1st

May 2nd

I Matter

May 3rd

May 4th

May 5th

May 6th

I Matter

Julia Keys and Jacqui Coles

May 7th

May 8th

May 9th

May 10th

I Matter

May 11th

May 12th

May 13th

May 14th

I Matter

May 15th

May 16th

May 17th

May 18th

I Matter

May 19th

May 20th

May 21st

May 22nd

I Matter

May 23rd

May 24th

May 25th

May 26th

I Matter

May 27th

May 28th

May 29th

May 30th

I Matter

May 31st

June

BRAVE!

$\mathcal{B}$ e responsible for the choices you make

$\mathcal{R}$ elease negative emotions

$\mathcal{A}$ waken your power

$\mathcal{V}$ ictory is yours

$\mathcal{E}$ mpower the strength within you

I Matter

June 1st

June 2nd

June 3rd

June 4th

I Matter

June 5th

June 6th

June 7th

June 8th

I Matter

June 9th

June 10th

June 11th

June 12th

I Matter

June 13th

June 14th

June 15th

June 16th

I Matter

June 17th

June 18th

June 19th

June 20th

I Matter

June 21st

June 22nd

My Freedom Diary & Journal

June 23rd

June 24th

I Matter

June 25th

June 26th

June 27th

June 28th

I Matter

June 29th

June 30th

July

VISION

V isualise a happy future

I nvest your time wisely

S ee beyond your fears

I nspire your creativity

O pen your heart and mind to new experiences

N o is an okay word to say to others

I Matter

July 1st

July 2nd

July 3rd

July 4th

I Matter

July 5th

July 6th

July 7th

July 8th

I Matter

July 9th

July 10th

July 11th

July 12th

I Matter

July 13th

July 14th

July 15th

July 16th

I Matter

July 17th

July 18th

July 19th

July 20th

I Matter

July 21st

July 22nd

July 23rd

July 24th

I Matter

July 25th

July 26th

July 27th

July 28th

I Matter

July 29th

July 30th

July 31st

I Matter

AUGUST
SAFE

$\mathcal{S}$ ecure your boundaries

$\mathcal{A}$ ccept only what you feel comfortable with

$\mathcal{F}$ eel the fear and push forward

$\mathcal{E}$ very defeat is only a minor setback

August 1st

August 2nd

I Matter

August 3rd

August 4th

August 5th

August 6th

I Matter

August 7th

August 8th

August 9th

August 10th

I Matter

August 11th

August 12th

August 13th

August 14th

I Matter

August 15th

August 16th

August 17th

August 18th

I Matter

August 19th

August 20th

August 21st

August 22nd

I Matter

August 23rd

August 24th

August 25th

August 26th

I Matter

August 27th

August 28th

August 29th

August 30th

I Matter

August 31st

September

TRUST

T ake comfort, knowing others trust you

R estore your belief in your own judgements

U nconditional love is only for those who deserve it

S elf-belief comes with knowing who you are

T ime is a great healer

September 1st

September 2nd

September 3rd

September 4th

I Matter

September 5th

September 6th

September 7th

September 8th

I Matter

September 9th

September 10th

September 11th

September 12th

I Matter

September 13th

September 14th

September 15th

September 16th

I Matter

September 17th

September 18th

September 19th

September 20th

I Matter

September 21st

September 22nd

September 23rd

September 24th

I Matter

September 25th

September 26th

September 27th

September 28th

I Matter

September 29th

September 30th

October

BELIEVE

$\mathcal{B}$ egin each day with a grateful thought

$\mathcal{E}$ very day you are getting stronger

$\mathcal{L}$ ove yourself first—others can wait

$\mathcal{I}$ t's your life, live it your way

$\mathcal{E}$ xciting things can happen

$\mathcal{V}$ anquish self-doubt

$\mathcal{E}$ ven in the dark times good can happen

I Matter

October 1st

October 2nd

October 3rd

October 4th

I Matter

October 5th

October 6th

October 7th

October 8th

I Matter

October 9th

October 10th

October 11th

October 12th

I Matter

October 13th

October 14th

October 15th

October 16th

I Matter

October 17th

October 18th

October 19th

October 20th

I Matter

October 21st

October 22nd

October 23rd

October 24th

I Matter

October 25th

October 26th

October 27th

October 28th

I Matter

October 29th

October 30th

October 31st

I Matter

November

JOY

J ust because your heart is broken, doesn't mean it can't be mended

O ur thoughts are limitless

Y ou are loved

November 1st

November 2nd

I Matter

November 3rd

November 4th

November 5th

November 6th

I Matter

November 7th

November 8th

November 9th

November 10th

I Matter

November 11th

November 12th

November 13th

November 14th

I Matter

November 15th

November 16th

November 17th

November 18th

I Matter

November 19th

November 20th

November 21st

November 22nd

I Matter

November 23rd

November 24th

November 25th

November 26th

I Matter

November 27th

November 28th

November 29th

November 30th

I Matter

December

FREEDOM

$\mathcal{F}$ orgiveness sets you free

$\mathcal{R}$ ecovery is happening with every word you write

$\mathcal{E}$ nough is enough when you decide it is

$\mathcal{E}$ very new day leaves yesterday behind

$\mathcal{D}$ etach and be free

$\mathcal{O}$ nwards and upwards

$\mathcal{M}$ ake your dreams come true—you can do it!

December 1st

December 2nd

I Matter

December 3rd

December 4th

December 5th

December 6th

I Matter

December 7th

December 8th

December 9th

December 10th

I Matter

December 11th

December 12th

December 13th

December 14th

I Matter

December 15th

December 16th

December 17th

December 18th

I Matter

December 19th

December 20th

December 21st

December 22nd

I Matter

December 23rd

December 24th
Christmas Eve

A Special Note About Christmas

The media-driven image of Christmas magic and family bliss, brings high expectations and enormous pressure. Facing a relationship difficulty or break-up can feel overwhelming at any time, but is even harder over the Christmas period, when there is such a spotlight on perfection and happiness. This is especially the case if your ex is with someone new.

At Christmas, please remember to:

- Keep things in perspective. Despite the build up to Christmas, it only lasts a few days and you will get through it!
- Stay away from social media.
- Focus on the present and don't let your mind constantly stray back to happier times. Keep looking forward.
- Do accept how you are feeling and be kind to yourself. It's OK to have a cry and feel sad, in fact, it's quite normal.
- Focus on someone else. Try and make someone else happy.
- Don't isolate yourself. If friends/family invite you to join them, think twice before automatically saying, "No." They wouldn't have asked if they didn't want to be with you.
- Plan ahead. If you have children with your ex-partner, plan when in the Christmas period you will have the children. You can then plan ahead to make sure you are not alone when your children are with your ex-partner.

- If you are still together with your partner, but "pretending" for other people, make sure you lay out the ground rules with your partner about what you will and won't accept, and also what you expect from him/her
- Write down how you are feeling. Plan or re-visit your goals. They will help you to keep moving forward.

December 25th
Christmas Day

December 26th
Boxing Day

December 27th

December 28th

December 29th

December 30th

December 31st
New Year's Eve—Have hope for the future

Moving Forward...

We hope that by working through My Freedom Diary & Journal, it has helped you to move forward. We know it takes time, we are all different and some of us take longer to heal than others. We do not underestimate for a minute how tough it is. If you are still feeling overwhelmed and as though you are stuck, don't be disheartened, it's a process and you set the pace.

You can take the outlines, templates, ideas and structure of this book to create your own journal or diary. You can take the gratitude notes into your future diaries for example, or you could create your own journals based on your learnings throughout this journey.

However you move forward, we hope that the time you've spent with the My Freedom Diary & Journal has helped you on your path to happiness.

If you still feel stuck and you haven't already, now may be the time to seek professional help. Your GP is the best person for you to talk to at first, or you could discuss your feelings with a counsellor.

You can contact us personally at our website or email:
www.keys2life.co.uk or hello@keys2life.co.uk

You can do it. You can be happy

Keep looking forward

"Just go out there
and do what you've got to do."
Martina Navratilova

I Matter

About the Authors

Julia Keys and Jacqui Coles are the co-founders of the website www.keys2life.co.uk. They first became friends as teenagers, and although their lives took separate paths, fate always brought them together again. Frequently, those reunions occurred in the most unexpected of places and at times when one of them was struggling with an issue in their life. A true friend is there when you need them and none more so than when you are dealing with the effects of being in a relationship crisis. Julia and Jacqui's friendship has been their survival mechanism and they hope that anyone reading this book will feel their genuine desire to be their friend on every page.

Julia Keys has a professional background in nursing, counselling and psychotherapy; her specialist subjects include dealing with relationships, mental health issues and eating disorders. Julia was a school counsellor for five years, helping eleven to eighteen-year-old girls with myriad concerns, many of which related to their parent's relationship issues. Julia is skilled in safeguarding children and vulnerable adults. She has also worked at a specialist woman's centre where referrals came from all walks of life.

Jacqui Coles is a registered nurse, midwife and health visitor. Jacqui has a Bachelor's degree in Community Health and has supported many families dealing with the impact of a relationship crisis. She has extensive experience in safeguarding, patient safety, and as an advocate working in the NHS as a senior manager. In 2014, she became Deputy Chief Executive at the Patients Association, a high profile 'patient voice' charity. Jacqui has dealt with many situations where the client's personal relationship had been strained, broken down or challenged, influencing the individual's physical and mental wellbeing and ultimately, their recovery.

The Amazon and Waterstones bestselling infidelity survival guide is out now!

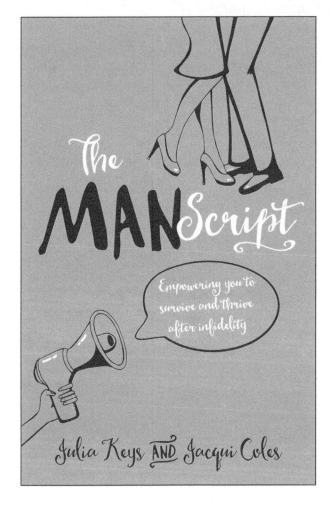

The MAN*Script*

The MAN*Script* is the ultimate guide to surviving and thriving after infidelity by Julia Keys (ex-wife of TV presenter Richard Keys) and Jacqui Coles. There is a script to infidelity, it's repeated time and time again, and this book will help you identify that script....and more. This is NOT a man-bashing book, the aim is to help those who have been cheated on to feel empowered rather than weakened by their experiences.

Filled with real life testimonials, The MAN*Script* will help you navigate the tumultuous times to come out stronger and happier.

"The MANScript certainly resonates with a large number of women! I am sure The MANScript will be a great success."
- Dear Deirdre, The Sun newspaper agony aunt -

"Fantastic book! The authors have taken a subject close to many people's hearts and have managed to tackle a difficult subject with great sensitivity, warmth and humour!"
- Independent Amazon review -

"A brilliant book that will definitely help women get through the grief of infidelity. A must read"
- Independent Amazon review -

Notes

Keep Looking Forward

Notes

I Matter

Notes

Notes

Notes

Notes

Notes